THE
GLOW·IN·THE·DARK
NIGHT SKY
BOOK

foreword by Heather Couper

Clint Hatchett

illustrated by Stephen Marchesi

HEINEMANN · LONDON

First published in the UK in 1989 by William Heinemann Ltd,
Michelin House, 81 Fulham Road, London SW3 6RB.
Foreword copyright © 1989 Heather Couper.
Text copyright © 1988 Random House, Inc.
Illustrations copyright © 1988 Stephen Marchesi.
All rights reserved.
ISBN 0 434 94224 3

Are you one of those people who says: "I'd love to take up stargazing, but I can't tell one star from another"? Then stay right here. This book is for you.

Thousands of years ago, our ancestors were faced with the same problem. In those days, there was no streetlighting or industrial pollution. The night skies were so clear that you were dazzled by stars. To make sense of it all, people picked out the brightest stars in the sky – and joined them up like a giant dot-to-dot puzzle. The shapes they drew up were called "constellations" (star-groups).

Every culture had its own way of joining up the dots, and so each had its own constellations. The people in Ancient China divided the sky up into hundreds of tiny constellations. In Australia, the Aborigines had such clear skies that they saw great clouds of stars. Their constellations – like "the Emu" – were dark places between the starclouds, where few stars were visible.

The patterns we know today started off life in the Near East, and spread along the shores of the Mediterranean Sea. The Babylonians and Greeks were great story-tellers. They peopled the sky with the heroes and heroines – and some of the villains – of their legends. (You can read some of their stories on the last page of this book.) Later on, Arab astronomers gave the brightest stars individual names – tongue-twisters like Betelgeuse, which people once (wrongly!) translated as "the armpit of the Sacred One".

Our ancestors didn't join up the stars just for fun. They actually depended on the stars. For instance, they used the regular rising and setting of the stars (caused by the Earth's rotation) to provide them with a clock. Every season brought different stars – which they used as signals to tell them when best to plant or harvest their crops. Out on the high seas, sailors used the stars to navigate by – sometimes, like the Polynesians, voyaging for thousands of miles out of sight of land with just the stars to guide them.

Today, we no longer rely on the stars for matters of life and death. But it's somehow reassuring to be able to go out at night and know which star is which. You really feel you're amongst old friends.

HOW TO USE THIS BOOK

The problem with most starmaps is that they're difficult to use outside at night! But the maps in this book are different: like the stars, they glow in the dark.

You need first to pick the right starmap for the time of year. The stars you see change every season. That's because our viewing platform is moving: as the Earth circles the Sun, we look out in different directions in space.

Next, is it the beginning of the season or the end? Each season has two maps: one for early, one for late. On your chosen map, look at the time chart in the bottom corner. This tells you roughly when the map will match what you see in the sky (times in summer are British Summer Time).

Each double-page spread has two maps of the whole sky. The one on the left is a simple chart showing the outlines of the constellation patterns you'll see at that time of year. The right-hand chart reveals the amazing creatures that our ancestors imagined amongst the stars.

You'll also notice that the starmaps have the points of the compass marked on them. Before you use the maps at night, make sure you know your compass directions from the place you're intending to stargaze. On a sunny day, there's an easy way to find out. When it's midday (1.00pm when we're on BST), stand with your back to the Sun. Since the Sun is due south at midday, your shadow is pointing north – and so east is to your right, west to your left. Mark these directions at your observing site!

Now you're all set. Before you go out, hold your starmap up to a bright light for a few minutes to make the stars glow. Then wrap up warm, grab a torch, and out you go! Once you're outside, wait a couple of minutes for your eyes to get used to the dark. Now face south, and turn the map until south is at the bottom. Then raise the map above your head, and compare its glowing patterns with the real thing in the sky. (If *your* stars stop glowing, you can recharge them with your torch.)

Can you spot the Great Bear? She's on view all the year round. In summer, you can pick out the stars of the Summer Triangle – or you can look for the long neck and outstretched wings of Cygnus, the Swan. In wintertime, Orion – the mighty hunter – rules the heavens.

With practice, you should be able to find all the constellations in this book – more than thirty in all. And on cloudy nights, you'll still be able to amaze your friends with your own private star-show!

Heather Couper

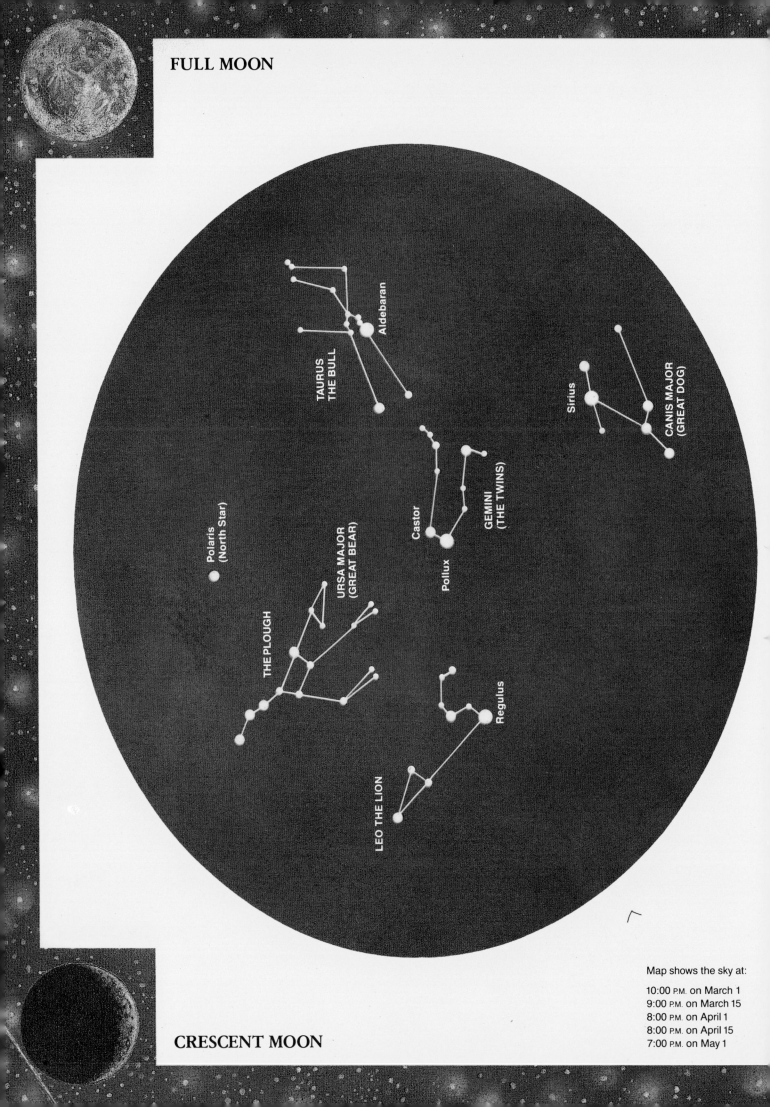

FULL MOON

TAURUS
THE BULL

Aldebaran

Sirius

CANIS MAJOR
(GREAT DOG)

Castor

GEMINI
(THE TWINS)

Polaris
(North Star)

URSA MAJOR
(GREAT BEAR)

Pollux

THE PLOUGH

Regulus

LEO THE LION

CRESCENT MOON

Map shows the sky at:

10:00 P.M. on March 1
9:00 P.M. on March 15
8:00 P.M. on April 1
8:00 P.M. on April 15
7:00 P.M. on May 1

EARLY SPRING

GIBBOUS MOON

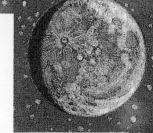

FIRST-QUARTER
MOON

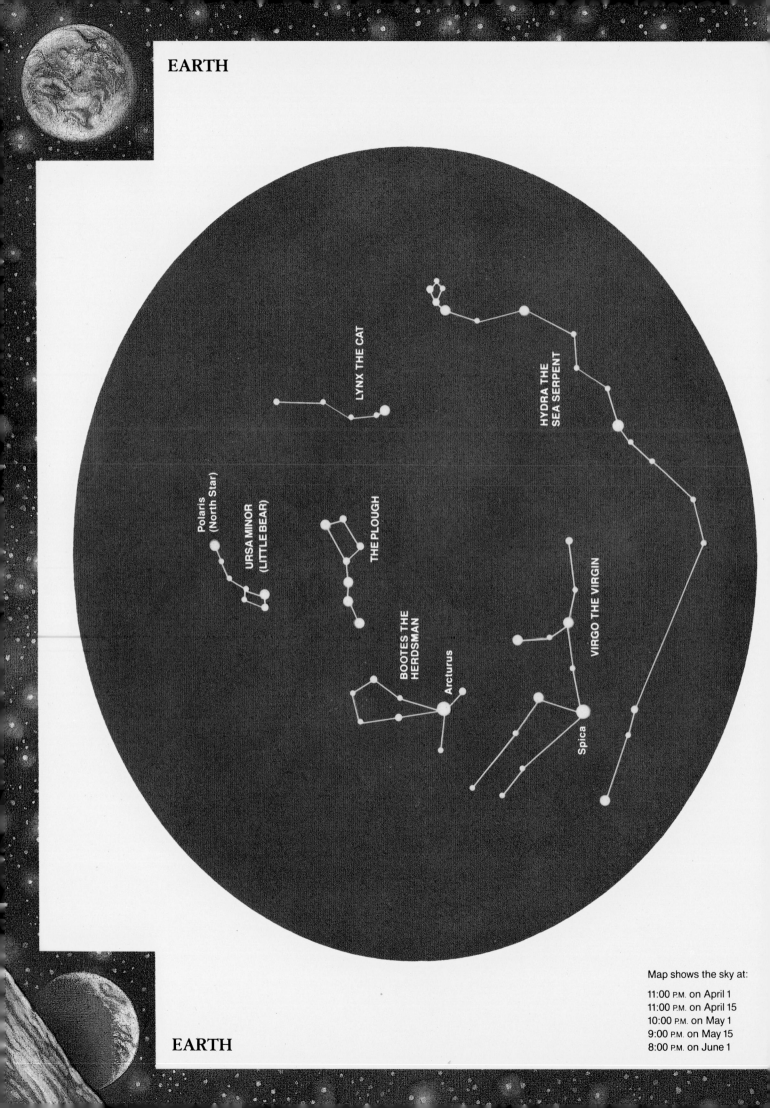

EARTH

LYNX THE CAT

HYDRA THE
SEA SERPENT

Polaris
(North Star)

URSA MINOR
(LITTLE BEAR)

THE PLOUGH

VIRGO THE VIRGIN

BOOTES THE
HERDSMAN

Arcturus

Spica

EARTH

Map shows the sky at:

11:00 P.M. on April 1
11:00 P.M. on April 15
10:00 P.M. on May 1
9:00 P.M. on May 15
8:00 P.M. on June 1

THE SUN

TOTAL ECLIPSE
OF THE SUN

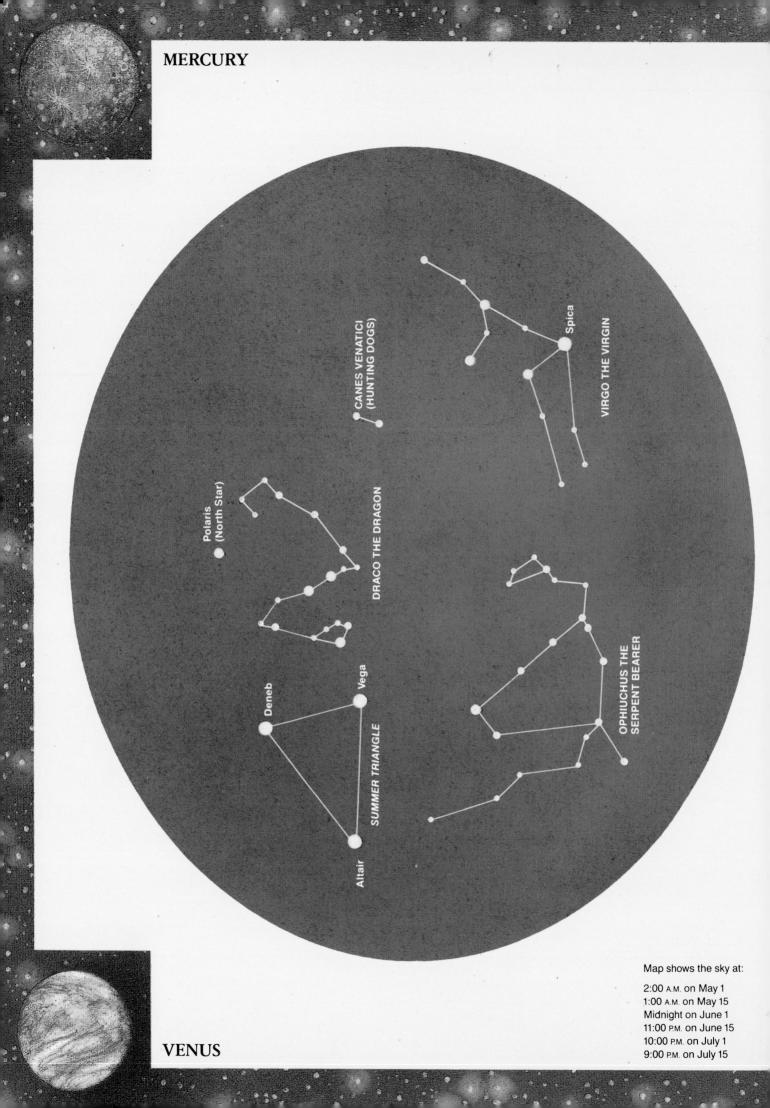

MERCURY

VENUS

CANES VENATICI
(HUNTING DOGS)

Spica

VIRGO THE VIRGIN

Polaris
(North Star)

DRACO THE DRAGON

Deneb

Vega

SUMMER TRIANGLE

Altair

OPHIUCHUS THE
SERPENT BEARER

Map shows the sky at:

2:00 A.M. on May 1
1:00 A.M. on May 15
Midnight on June 1
11:00 P.M. on June 15
10:00 P.M. on July 1
9:00 P.M. on July 15

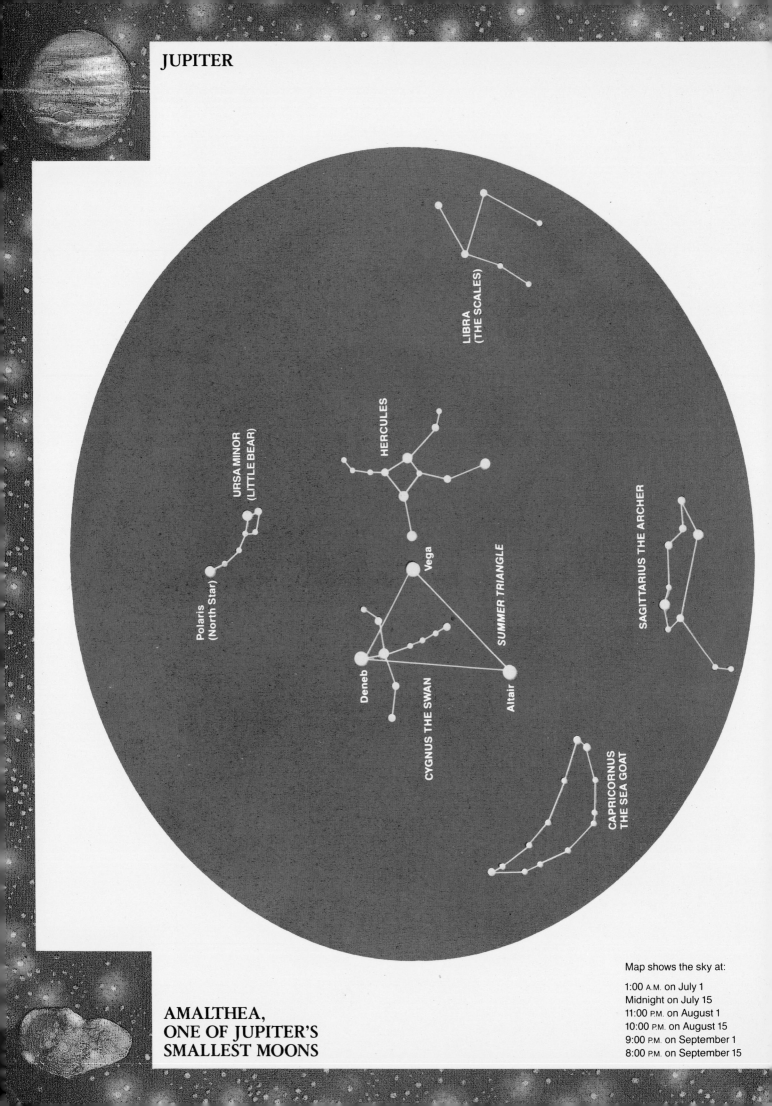

JUPITER

AMALTHEA,
ONE OF JUPITER'S
SMALLEST MOONS

LIBRA
(THE SCALES)

HERCULES

URSA MINOR
(LITTLE BEAR)

Polaris
(North Star)

Vega

SAGITTARIUS THE ARCHER

SUMMER TRIANGLE

Deneb

CYGNUS THE SWAN

Altair

CAPRICORNUS
THE SEA GOAT

Map shows the sky at:

1:00 A.M. on July 1
Midnight on July 15
11:00 P.M. on August 1
10:00 P.M. on August 15
9:00 P.M. on September 1
8:00 P.M. on September 15

IO, MOON OF JUPITER

EUROPA,
MOON OF JUPITER

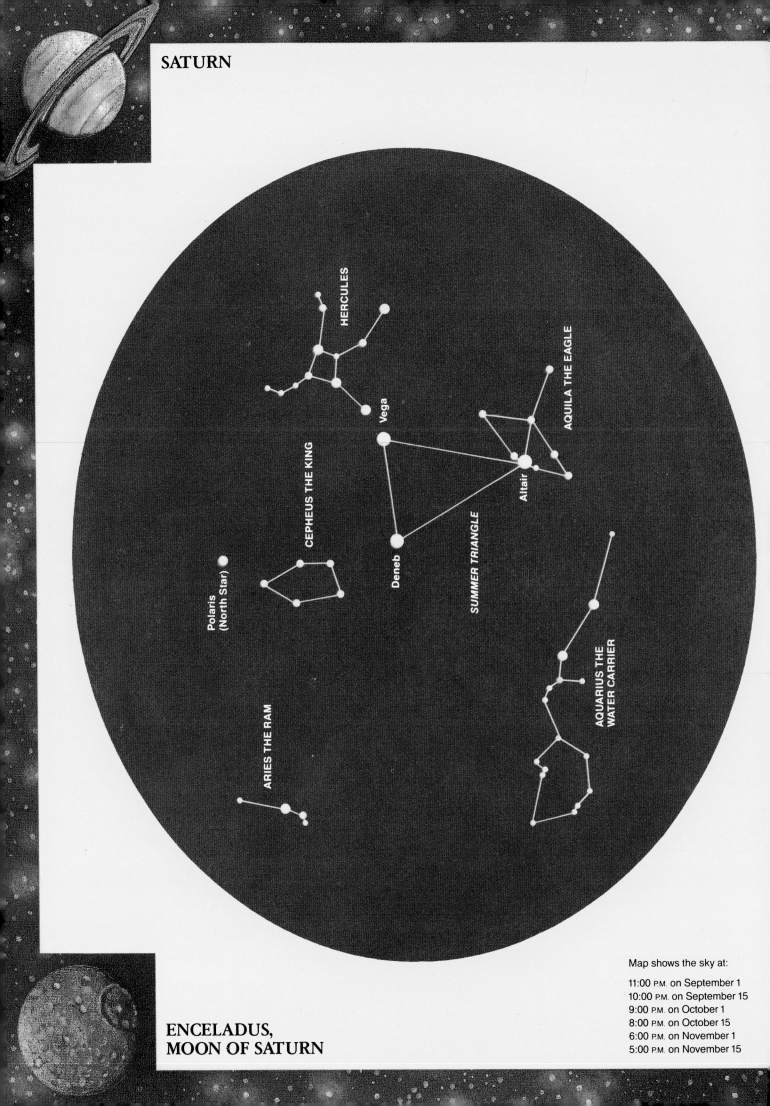

SATURN

HERCULES

AQUILA THE EAGLE

Vega

CEPHEUS THE KING

SUMMER TRIANGLE

Altair

Deneb

Polaris
(North Star)

AQUARIUS THE
WATER CARRIER

ARIES THE RAM

ENCELADUS,
MOON OF SATURN

Map shows the sky at:

11:00 P.M. on September 1
10:00 P.M. on September 15
9:00 P.M. on October 1
8:00 P.M. on October 15
6:00 P.M. on November 1
5:00 P.M. on November 15

EARLY AUTUMN

DIONE,
MOON OF SATURN

W
N · S
E

TITAN,
SATURN'S LARGEST MOON

URANUS

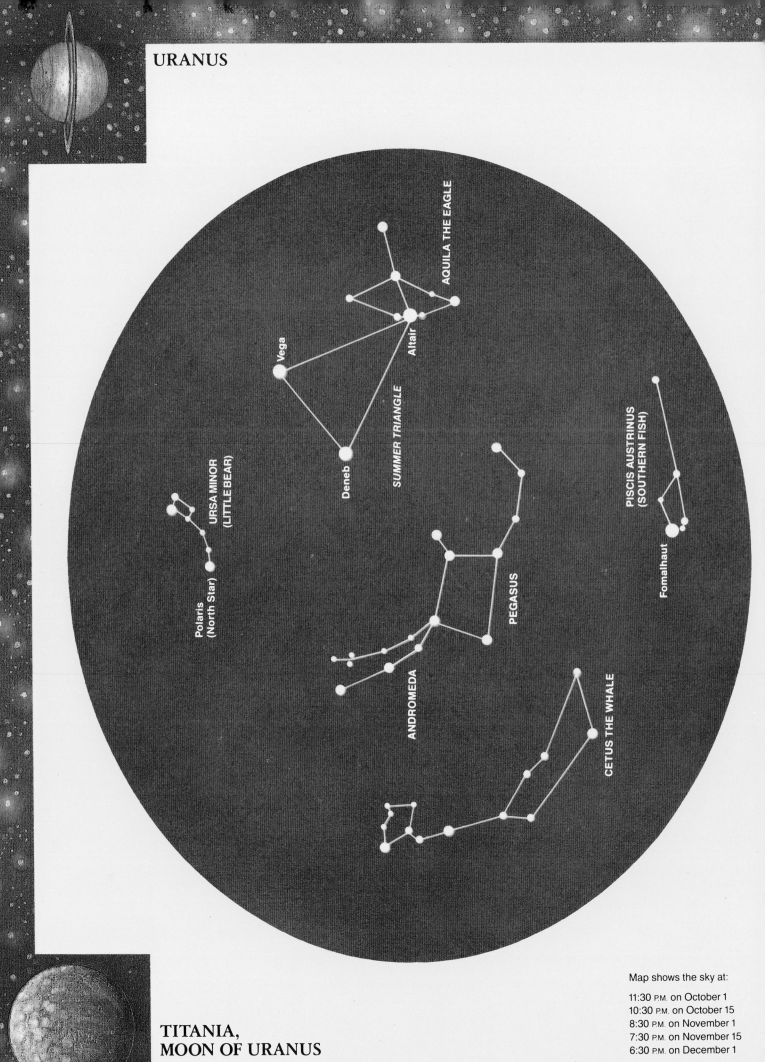

AQUILA THE EAGLE

Vega

Altair

SUMMER TRIANGLE

Deneb

URSA MINOR
(LITTLE BEAR)

Polaris
(North Star)

PISCIS AUSTRINUS
(SOUTHERN FISH)

Fomalhaut

PEGASUS

ANDROMEDA

CETUS THE WHALE

Map shows the sky at:

11:30 P.M. on October 1
10:30 P.M. on October 15
8:30 P.M. on November 1
7:30 P.M. on November 15
6:30 P.M. on December 1

TITANIA,
MOON OF URANUS

LATE AUTUMN

NEPTUNE

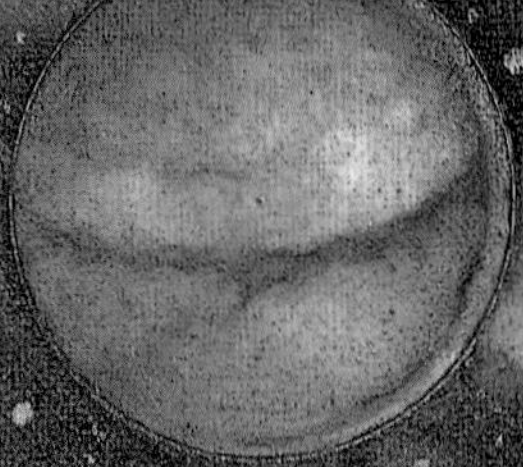

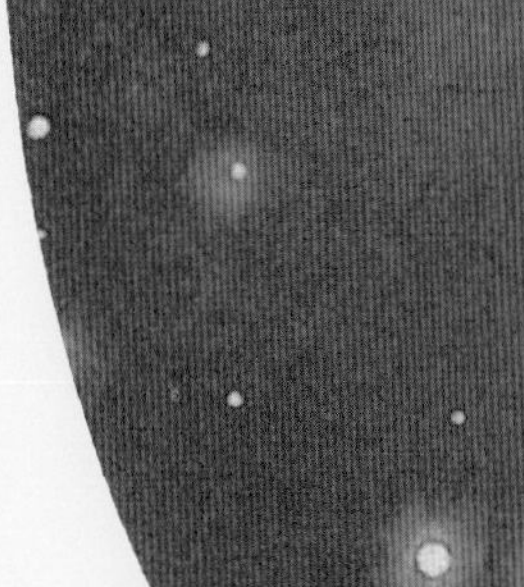

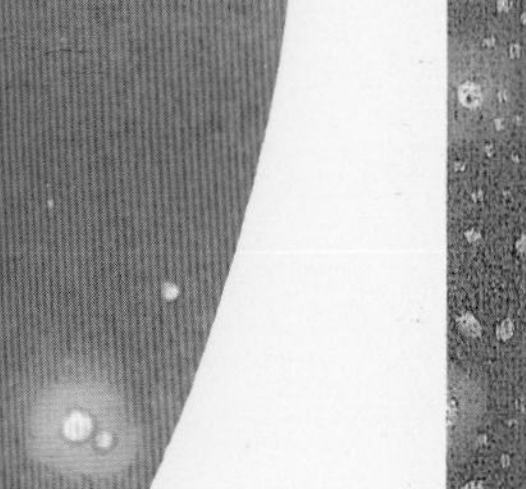

TRITON,
MOON OF NEPTUNE

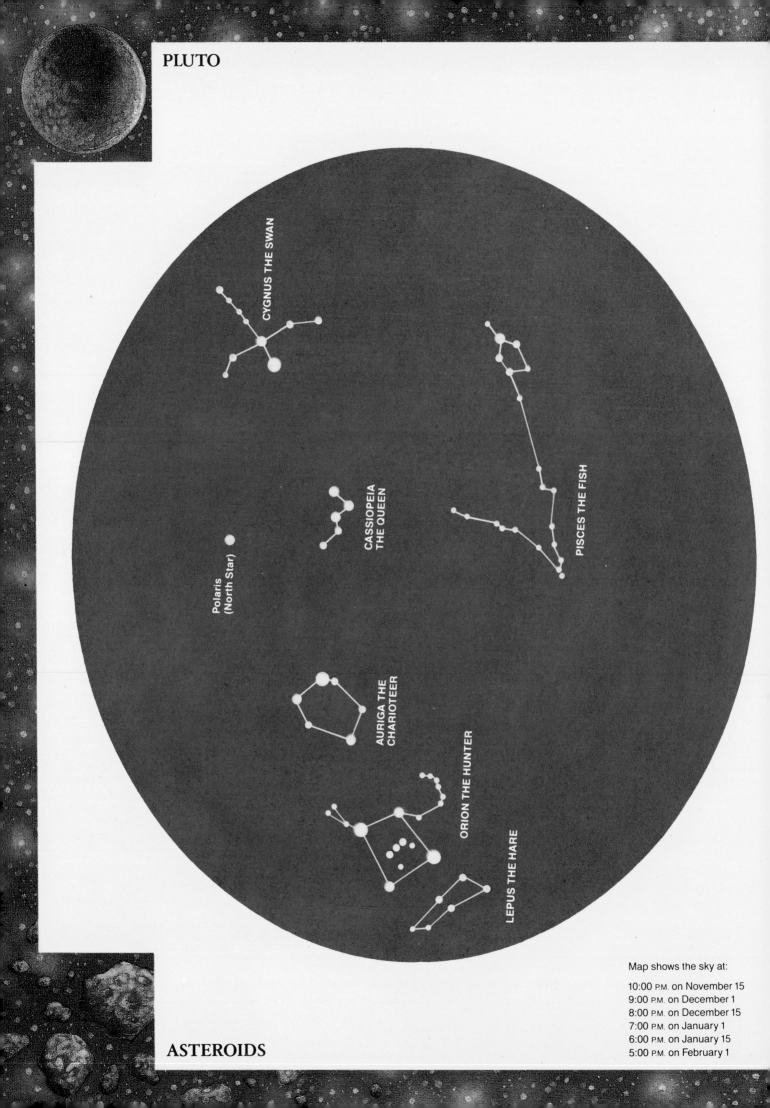

PLUTO

ASTEROIDS

CYGNUS THE SWAN

PISCES THE FISH

CASSIOPEIA
THE QUEEN

Polaris
(North Star)

AURIGA THE
CHARIOTEER

ORION THE HUNTER

LEPUS THE HARE

Map shows the sky at:

10:00 P.M. on November 15
9:00 P.M. on December 1
8:00 P.M. on December 15
7:00 P.M. on January 1
6:00 P.M. on January 15
5:00 P.M. on February 1

EARLY WINTER

HALLEY'S COMET

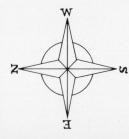

COMET KOHOUTEK

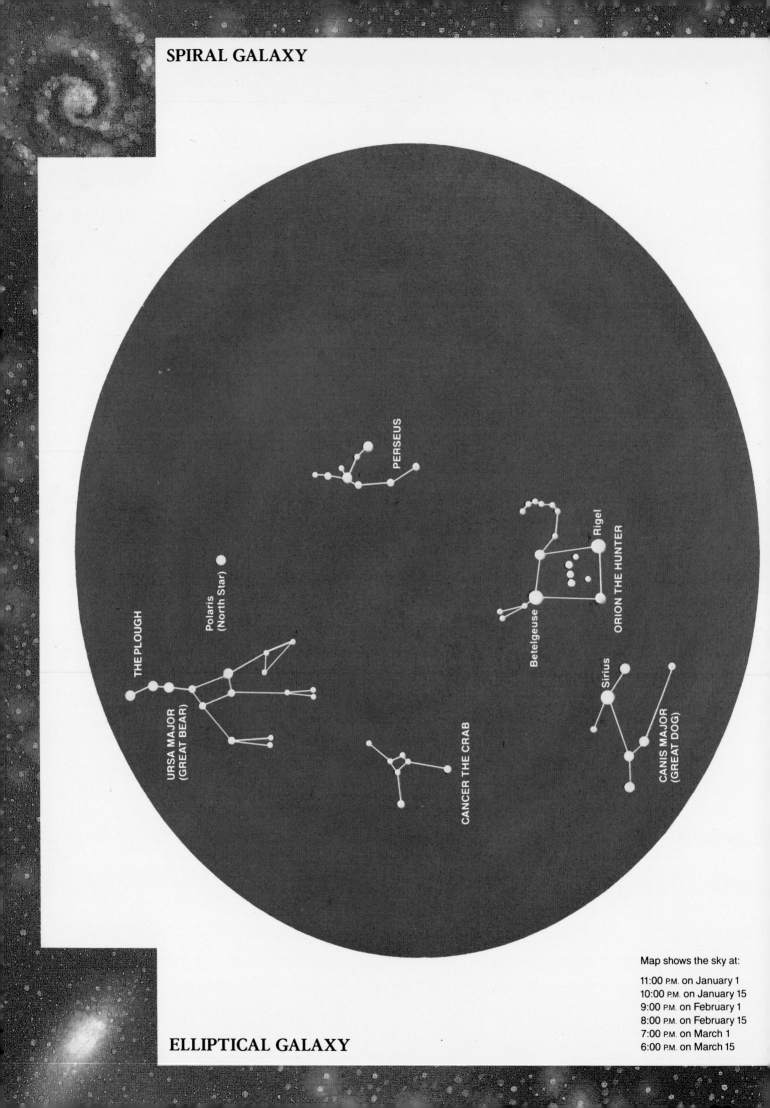

SPIRAL GALAXY

ELLIPTICAL GALAXY

PERSEUS

Polaris
(North Star)

THE PLOUGH

URSA MAJOR
(GREAT BEAR)

Rigel

Betelgeuse

ORION THE HUNTER

Sirius

CANIS MAJOR
(GREAT DOG)

CANCER THE CRAB

Map shows the sky at:

11:00 P.M. on January 1
10:00 P.M. on January 15
9:00 P.M. on February 1
8:00 P.M. on February 15
7:00 P.M. on March 1
6:00 P.M. on March 15

LATE WINTER

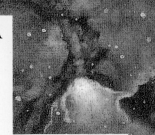

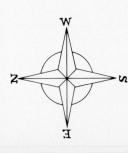

ABOUT THE CONSTELLATIONS

Andromeda. In Greek legends, Andromeda was the daughter of CASSIOPEIA and CEPHEUS. PERSEUS saved her from the sea monster CETUS.

Aquarius (the Water Carrier). The Babylonians saw this group of stars as a man pouring water from a jar.

Aquila (the Eagle). A companion of Jupiter, the king of the Roman gods.

Aries (the Ram). The golden fleece of this ram was the prize carried off by the Greek hero Jason, leader of the Argonauts.

Auriga (the Charioteer). A legendary king of Athens, Greece, who was said to have invented the chariot.

Boötes (the Herdsman). With his two dogs (CANES VENATICI), Boötes chases the Great Bear and the Little Bear (URSA MAJOR and URSA MINOR) around the sky.

Cancer (the Crab). A monster in Greek legends who attacked HERCULES while he was fighting the sea serpent HYDRA.

Canes Venatici (the Hunting Dogs). BOÖTES the herdsman's two dogs (see above).

Canis Major (the Great Dog). The faithful companion of ORION the hunter.

Capricornus (the Sea Goat). In the legends of many cultures, this creature, with the head of a goat and the tail of a fish, could travel on both land and sea.

Cassiopeia and **Cepheus.** The queen and king of Ethiopia; parents of ANDROMEDA. The main stars of Cassiopeia form a rough W shape.

Cetus (the Whale). The sea monster that nearly ate ANDROMEDA before she was rescued by PERSEUS. Cetus was turned to stone when Perseus flashed the head of Medusa at him.

Cygnus (the Swan). Greek legends say that Zeus, the king of the gods, sometimes disguised himself as a swan.

Draco (the Dragon). This constellation has been associated with many legendary monsters. One of them is a dragon killed by HERCULES.

Gemini (the Twins). The twins were Castor and Pollux, two devoted brothers in Greek legends.

Hercules. To the ancient Greeks, Hercules was the strongest and bravest man on earth. He killed many monsters, some of whom also became constellations (see CANCER, DRACO, HYDRA, and LEO).

Hydra (the Sea Serpent). A many-headed monster killed by HERCULES. Hydra is the largest constellation in the sky.

Leo (the Lion). The fiercest lion in the world.

No weapons would wound him. HERCULES solved that problem by choking the life out of him.

Lepus (the Hare). While being hunted by ORION, Lepus the hare slipped between his feet to hide.

Libra (the Scales). To the Romans, this group of stars represented the scales of justice.

Lynx (the Cat). This constellation was named Lynx because only those with eyes as keen as a lynx's will be able to find it.

Ophiuchus (the Serpent Bearer). Ancient people saw in this group of stars the shape of a man holding a huge snake.

Orion (the Hunter). The brightest and most easily recognized constellation in the winter sky. Orion was the companion of Artemis, Greek goddess of the hunt.

Pegasus. This is the winged horse that appeared from the body of Medusa when Perseus beheaded her.

Perseus. The Greek hero who, among other brave deeds, killed the monster Medusa. Medusa's face was so horrible that anyone who looked at her turned instantly to stone.

Pisces (the Fish). Pisces represents Venus, the Roman goddess of love and beauty, and her son Cupid. To escape from a monster, they turned into fish and jumped into a river.

Pisces Austrinus (the Southern Fish). A constellation with only one bright star. It is sometimes shown drinking water being poured by AQUARIUS.

Sagittarius (the Archer). This constellation is usually shown as a centaur – a creature that was half man, half horse – aiming his bow and arrow at a giant scorpion.

Summer Triangle. Not a constellation but a triangle made up of three bright stars from three different constellations: Vega (in Lyra, the Lyre), Altair (in AQUILA), and Deneb (in CYGNUS).

Taurus (the Bull). In Greek myth, Zeus disguised himself as a snow-white bull in order to win the heart of a princess.

Ursa Major (the Great Bear). When Zeus fell in love with Callisto, his jealous wife changed Callisto into a bear. Ursa Major includes the Plough, the best-known group of stars in the sky.

Ursa Minor (the Little Bear). Callisto and Zeus had a son, whom Zeus changed into a bear and put in the sky. Ursa Minor includes Polaris, the North Star.

Virgo (the Virgin). The Greek goddess of justice. This constellation has also been associated with Ceres, goddess of the harvest.